Contents

Published by Coordination Group Publications.
Text, design, layout and illustrations © Richard Parsons 1999.
All rights reserved.

ISBN 1 84146 065 6

Groovy website: www.cgpbooks.co.uk
Printed by Butler & Tanner Ltd, Frome and London
Clipart sources: CorelDRAW and VECTOR.

0899

Intro to the Series

Yet another series of maths books. But these are different. We've kept the same chatty style that was so successful in our previous KS2 maths books, but this time we've tailored a whole course to precisely match the Numeracy Strategy Framework. Here's some of the top features of the series:

- Separate homework and classwork books. No more, "Miss, I left my book at home, I'll have to share."
- The classwork books match the Numeracy Strategy and the Framework within it. Use these books and you're automatically following the Numeracy Strategy.
- The homework books match the order of the classwork books. So it's easy to set homework.
- The books have been written to complement your teaching. They give ideal practice questions and bits of explanation along the way to reinforce what you've taught.
- All the books can be written in, leaving pupils with a handy record of the year's work. Or you could issue exercise books and reuse our books.
- Our Year 3 & 4 books are carefully written to tackle the 'Year 3 & 4 black spot'. Too many publishers have ignored this age group or produced dry books that do nothing to inspire children. Our books aim to redress the balance.
- The Teacher's Handbook — loads of activities for easy reference.

...and if you're not convinced after that lot, just try them out:
We've sent free sample copies to every primary school,
and the start of each year is available on the Internet at

www.cgpbooks.co.uk

Buy our books — they're ace

Intro to this Book

Guide to Levels

In the Numeracy Strategy document from QCA, there's very little mention of levels. But in the Programme of Study they are very important. More importantly for you, the SAT test at the end of KS2 is marked in terms of levels, and the Government has set a target that 75% of the children taking it will achieve Level 4 or higher by the year 2002. To help relate this to the Numeracy Strategy and our classwork and homework books, we have produced a guide to levels in maths at KS2.

The Programme of Study sets down the levels in four areas: Using and Applying Maths; Number and Algebra; Shape, Space and Measure; and Handling Data. However, most teaching is expected to be based on the Numeracy Strategy, which is organised in terms of the five strands defined in it. To make your job easier, we've arranged our notes on the levels into the five strands.

Note that they don't have to reach, say, level 3 in every area to be level 3 overall — it's the average that counts.

Activities

One thing that the Numeracy strategy is really keen on is activities; for pairs, small groups or the whole class. Thinking these up can be quite fun, but very time consuming. Sometimes when you need an activity for tomorrow, other things might be more pressing (like getting more than a couple of hours sleep).

That's where this section comes in. Not only have we put in loads of ideas for activities that help kids to learn, but there are photocopiable resources like game boards, too. You can even enlarge them when you photocopy them, to make them A4 or bigger.

Another thing that the activities are really useful for is differentiation. The Government stresses how important this is, but when you've got a full class, doing different work with each group is not exactly easy. The activities have variations, some to make them easier, some to make them more challenging, so you can set each group off on the same activity, but doing different versions. So while some are learning about grids, advanced ones could be learning coordinates, and younger kids could be consolidating number squares. Brilliant.

Level 2

This is round about where they should be at the start of Year 3. Some time in Year 3 can be spent on this stuff, but it's really meant to be revision.

Numbers and the Number System

First of all, they need to be able to count well.

They need to understand the place value system, and be able to use it to put 2-digit numbers in order of size.

Tougher than this, they have to be able to recognise sequences of numbers, including odd and even numbers.

They also have to know that − is the inverse of +, and be able to use this (_eg_ to check answers).

Calculations

They need to be able to talk about what they've done, with some mathematical words and a few symbols and easy diagrams — nothing too hard at this level.

They need to explain why an answer is right, again in fairly simple terms.

They also need to be able to use some mental calculation strategies to solve number problems, particularly involving money and measure (_eg_ grouping together numbers that add up to 10).

Make sure you get them learning these: They need to remember and use addition and subtraction facts up to 10.

Level 2

Solving Problems

They need to be able to work out what maths to use for a given *simple* problem — *eg* "I have 3 carrots and I buy 4 more; how many do I have now?"

In particular, they should be able to tell whether a problem in words means add or take away.

Measures, Shape and Space

Level 2 pupils should know the maths names for common 2-D and 3-D shapes.

They also have to be able to say what properties shapes have, *eg* how many sides, how many corners...

They should understand a bit about angles as turns, and be able to spot right angles.

They should be getting to grips with the common units for length and mass.

Handling Data

If a Level 2 student is given a load of objects, they need to be able to sort them, using more than one criterion.

They need to be able to collect their own information, and write it down in simple lists, tables and block graphs.

Level 3

The brightest ones may have touched on this at Key Stage 1, but really this is Key Stage 2 stuff. It's not even all over by the end of Year 3: there'll be a fair bit of this stuff in Year 4 and even a quick scan over it in Year 5.

Numbers and the Number System

They need to have place value figured out for numbers up to 1000. They should be able to use it to make approximations (eg 1293 to nearest 100).

They should be having a go at decimal notation, but they don't need to be too well-versed in it.

They should be able to recognise negative numbers, but as long as they're happy with them in contexts like temperature and money, they're doing fine.

They need to have got to grips with simple fractions with a numerator of more than one, and they should be able to see when two simple fractions are equivalent.

Calculations

More memorising: they should know addition and subtraction facts up to 20 and use them to solve problems with bigger numbers.

They need to have learnt the multiplication tables for 2, 3, 4, 5, and 10, and be able to use them to work out division facts.

They should have mastered whole number problems with × or ÷, including ones with remainders.

Adding and subtracting 2-digit numbers mentally should be easy enough for them, and 3-digit numbers should be OK with paper.

Level 3

Solving Problems

Now they have to figure out their own ways around difficulties that come up.

They need to be starting to organise their work, rather than just scribbling numbers all over the page.

They should be beginning to check answers, but they don't have to worry too much about formal ways of checking just yet.

They should be able to talk about their work and explain what they've done.

They should be happy with basic maths symbols and diagrams.

Given a general statement (*eg* all numbers ending in 0 are multiples of 10), they should be able to give an example (*eg* $40 = 4 \times 10$).

Measures, Shape and Space

Pupils need to be able to classify 3-D and 2-D shapes in different ways using things like symmetry.

They should be able to work with various units for length, capacity, mass and time — including the standard metric units.

Handling Data

They need to be able to get information from simple tables and lists.

They should be able to get information from bar charts and pictograms (where each picture can represent more than one object).

They also need to be able to draw bar charts, and pictograms in which each picture represents more than one object.

Level 4

This is the Holy Grail of Key Stage 2. The Government reckons that 75% of 11-year-olds should be at Level 4 or above by 2002. The Numeracy Strategy is written on the basis that pupils will reach Level 4 at the end of Year 6. If they're going to do that, they'll probably need to be starting it in Year 5 to give them time to get to grips with it. Fun, fun, fun.

Numbers and the Number System

They'll need to be able to recognise proportions of an object, and describe them with simple fractions and percentages.

By this stage it shouldn't be much of a problem to get them comfortable with number patterns so they can describe them.

They also need to get to grips with relationships between numbers, *eg* multiples, factors and squares.

Algebra makes its first real appearance here, with easy formulae in words. If they can cope with some simple examples, they'll be fine.

Calculations

They need to use their understanding of place value to × and ÷ whole numbers by 100.

They should be able to remember multiplication facts up to 10 × 10, and quickly work out the division facts that go with them.

They should also have got to grips with standard written methods for +, −, × and ÷. For × and ÷ it's OK if they can only manage *short* multiplication and division.

Decimals shouldn't be a problem by now — Level 4 pupils should be able to add and subtract decimals to 2 decimal places, and order them to 3 places.

Level 4

Solving Problems

To reach Level 4, kids need to be able to come up with their own ideas about how to tackle problems. This includes problems in which maths is applied to the real world.

Their presentation of results must be clear and organised.

When they've solved a problem, they should check if the answer is sensible in the context of the problem.

Measures, Shape and Space

Here comes the fun: they need to make 3-D models of shapes by sticking edges together, so give them plenty of practice with paper and glue or sticky tape.

Less excitingly, they need to be able to draw 2-D shapes on grids — and at an angle; not just in one position.

Given a mirror line, they should be able to reflect a simple shape.

By now they really need to be comfortable with units, and should be able to pick good ones to use for various things. They should also be able to pick the right instrument for a measurement, and give their readings to a sensible level of accuracy.

They need to figure out perimeters and areas of simple shapes. They should be happy using and interpreting coordinates in the first quadrant.

Handling Data

Things are getting a bit sophisticated now: they should be able to collect discrete data, recording it in a frequency table rather than just in a list.

They need to be able to use the mode and range when they're talking about their data.

They should be able to group data sensibly, with equal intervals, and draw frequency diagrams. They need to be able to interpret frequency diagrams.

They should be able to draw and interpret simple line graphs.

Level 5

If the Government is aiming for Level 4 at Year 6, you might think they don't need any Level 5. No way. The Government also reckons that they need to have a go at Level 5 in Year 6, so they are more solid with Level 4. It makes sense, but you probably want to concentrate on Level 4, and just give them a taster of this. Except for the really bright ones, of course.

Numbers and the Number System

This is fairly tough — to get to Level 5 they need a pretty solid understanding of numbers.

They also need to be able to add and subtract negative numbers, as well as being able to put them in order. It's still only in the context of something like temperature or money, though.

With fractions they need to be able to cancel common factors to put a fraction in its simplest form.

Ratio and proportion problems need to be cracked, though they'll only get fairly easy ones.

They should be able to work out a fraction or percentage of some amount, though for some of these problems they may use a calculator.

Algebra's getting under way now. They need to be able to make and use formulae with one or two operations, now using letters instead of just words.

Calculations

They should have place value down pat by now, and so should be able to $\times$ and $\div$ whole numbers and decimals by 10, 100, 1000.

Sums are fairly complete: they need to be able to do $+$, $-$, $\times$, and $\div$ with decimals of 1 or 2 decimal places.

Multiplying any 3-digit number by a 2-digit number without a calculator is one of the many joys of Level 5.

Solving Problems

To get to Level 5, kids need to go through a task as a whole. So they should be able to work out what information they need, then find it. Afterwards they should check their results.

They need to describe things using symbols, words and diagrams.

They should also be able to figure out their own conclusions, and explain how they got them.

They should be carefully checking answers, either by making an estimate or using inverses.

Measures, Shape and Space

They should be able to measure or draw angles to the nearest °.

They need to know that the angles in a triangle add up to 180°, and that angles around a point add up to 360°.

Given a 2-D shape, they should be able to find its symmetries.

They should be able to convert between various metric units, and have an idea of the sizes of the common imperial units.

They should be able to make sensible estimates of quantities in a variety of real-life situations.

They also need to know the formula for area of a rectangle, and be able to use it.

They need to be able to use coordinates in all four quadrants.

Handling Data

They should be able to use the mean, but only with discrete data.

They need to be able to compare two simple distributions using the mean, median, mode and range.

They should be able to interpret a range of different graphs and diagrams, including pie charts.

By now they should be beginning to use probability and understand the probability scale.

They should be able to work out probabilities of things with equally likely outcomes, or from experiments / surveys.

They should know that doing the same experiment twice doesn't necessarily give the same result.

Snakes and Ladders

<u>Maths</u>: Adding and subtracting, number squares
<u>Groups</u>: Pairs or small groups
<u>Equipment</u>: Counters, pair of dice, photocopies of board opposite

Rules:

Everyone has a counter (buttons, coins, or even rubbers and pencil sharpeners are fine if you don't have any others). Start off with all of the counters on square 1. The players take it in turns to roll two dice and add up the total. They then count on that many places. If someone ends up on a snake's mouth, they slide down it to the end of its tail. If anyone gets to the foot of a ladder, they can climb to the top of it.

It's good practice to add the numbers on the dice, instead of counting on one lot, then the next lot. It also makes it pretty obvious that it doesn't matter which dice you count first, or which order you add them in.

You could sometimes ask everyone to work out how many places a player has moved ahead when they go up a ladder, or how many they lost when they slid down a snake. You could ask how far ahead the person in the lead is, or how far behind another player is.

Variations

To encourage the players to work out how far they've dropped down a ladder, you could add a rule — if they work it out they get another go, to make up for falling down the ladder. To make it a bit harder, the rule might only apply if they've fallen down an odd number of squares, say. Or if the number of squares they've fallen down is above 20, or...

Snakes and Ladders Board

FINISH 100	99	98	97	96	95	94	93	92	91
81	82	83	84	85	86	87	88	89	90
80	79	78	77	76	75	74	73	72	71
61	62	63	64	65	66	67	68	69	70
60	59	58	57	56	55	54	53	52	51
41	42	43	44	45	46	47	48	49	50
40	39	38	37	36	35	34	33	32	31
21	22	23	24	25	26	27	28	29	30
20	19	18	17	16	15	14	13	12	11
Start 1	2	3	4	5	6	7	8	9	10

Everyone starts on 1.

Each go, you move on the number you throw on the dice.

If you land on a snake's mouth, you slide down to the end of its tail.

If you land on the bottom of a ladder, you can climb to the top.

The first person to get to 100 wins.

Differences Card Game

Maths: Differences
Groups: Pairs
Equipment: Photocopies of cards from pages 15-17

A fairly simple game that gives good subtraction practice.

Rules

There are two players. The game uses a double set of the cards on the next three pages. Each player is dealt a stack of ten cards. Both players then choose one of their cards and slide it forward. They turn their cards over at the same time. Whoever played the highest card wins that round. Their score, recorded on a separate sheet, is increased by the difference between the two cards.

If the two cards are the same, nobody wins the round.

Variations

Use a different number of cards.

Use cards with different numbers.

Put down two cards at once — the players have to add them up, or make them into a two-digit number. If they are made into a two-digit number, it must be clear beforehand which number is to form which digit.

The score could be worked out in different ways. For example the cards could be added together for the score, or the points might depend on whether the sum or difference is even/odd/a prime/a square etc.

If a round is drawn, each player could instead keep the card they just played as the right-hand digit of a two-digit number (this works best if you're only using the digits 1-9). The players would then play a card to form the first digit. The winner and score would be worked out in the same way as before, but from two-digit numbers. The difference between these numbers could be huge, so it's worth trying to win any 'doubles' like this.

Cards for Differences Games

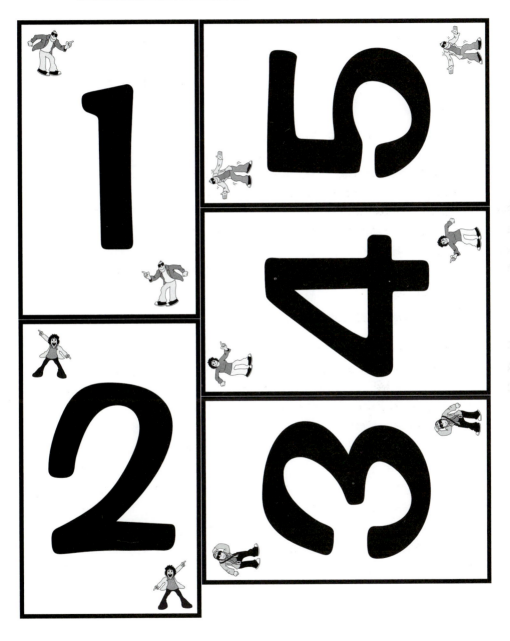

Cards for Differences Games

Cards for Differences Games

Sum Bingo

<u>Maths</u>: +, −, ×, ÷
<u>Groups</u>: Whole class
<u>Equipment</u>: Photocopies of cards from pages 19-25

What to do:

Everyone has a copy of one of the bingo cards. You call out the sums below, one at a time, and fairly slowly. Then everyone has to work out if they have the answer to that sum. If they do, they write the sum in the gap on the card. The first person to fill in every gap on the card has to shout "bingo", and wins (assuming they haven't made any mistakes).

Make sure you vary the order when you call the sums out, or the same card will win every time.

Variations

You could obviously use different sums and/or cards. That way the level of difficulty can be tailored to the class. The blank cards on page 64 can be used for this.

The answers on the cards could be covered up with counters or small bits of paper when their sums have been called. That way the cards could be reused — but you wouldn't be able to see where someone had gone wrong.

Sums to call out

3×4	9×8	5×5	$43 + 37$
$36 - 24$	12×3	7×8	$20 - 6$
$17 - 9$	$22 \div 2$	11×7	$50 \div 5$
$24 + 18$	$66 \div 3$	4×9	9×3
$59 - 13$	$18 + 22$	$56 - 18$	$45 - 15$
$37 + 24$	$79 - 19$	$88 - 44$	5×6
$31 - 19$	$64 - 21$	$50 \div 2$	6×4
7×6		$6 + 6$	

Cards for Sum Bingo

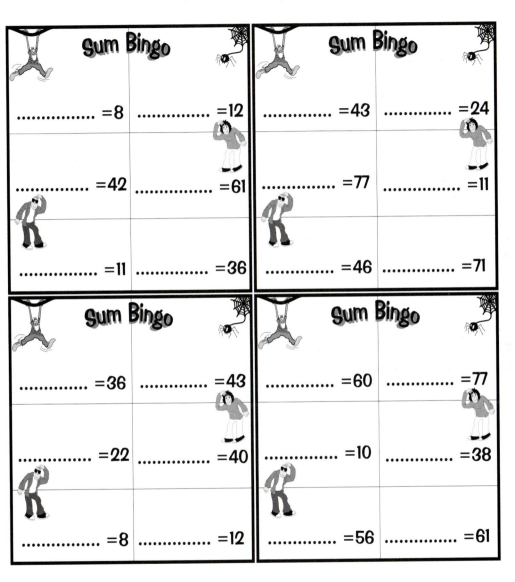

Sum Bingo

.... =8   .... =12

.... =42   .... =61

.... =11   .... =36

Sum Bingo

.... =43   .... =24

.... =77   .... =11

.... =46   .... =71

Sum Bingo

.... =36   .... =43

.... =22   .... =40

.... =8   .... =12

Sum Bingo

.... =60   .... =77

.... =10   .... =38

.... =56   .... =61

Cards for Sum Bingo

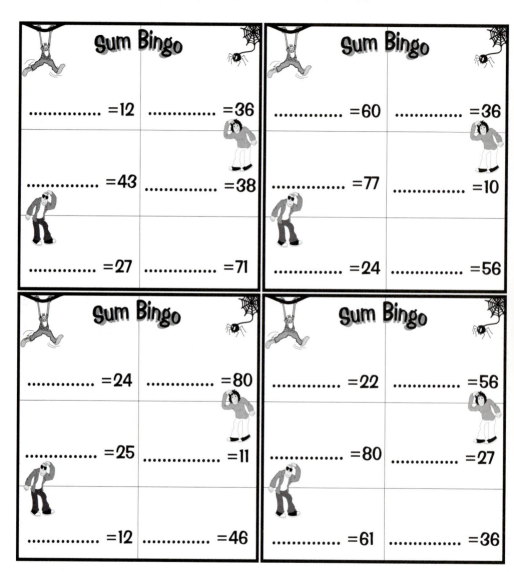

Sum Bingo

.... =12	.... =36
.... =43	.... =38
.... =27	.... =71

Sum Bingo

.... =60	.... =36
.... =77	.... =10
.... =24	.... =56

Sum Bingo

.... =24	.... =80
.... =25	.... =11
.... =12	.... =46

Sum Bingo

.... =22	.... =56
.... =80	.... =27
.... =61	.... =36

Cards for Sum Bingo

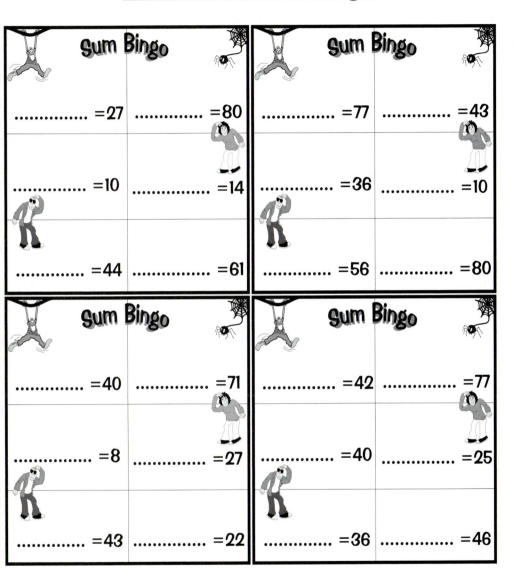

Sum Bingo

.... =27   .... =80

.... =10   .... =14

.... =44   .... =61

Sum Bingo

.... =77   .... =43

.... =36   .... =10

.... =56   .... =80

Sum Bingo

.... =40   .... =71

.... =8   .... =27

.... =43   .... =22

Sum Bingo

.... =42   .... =77

.... =40   .... =25

.... =36   .... =46

Cards for Sum Bingo

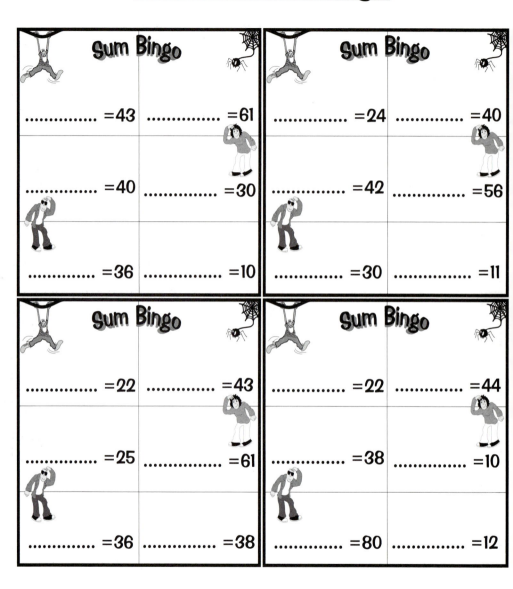

Sum Bingo

.... =43	.... =61
.... =40	.... =30
.... =36	.... =10

Sum Bingo

.... =24	.... =40
.... =42	.... =56
.... =30	.... =11

Sum Bingo

.... =22	.... =43
.... =25	.... =61
.... =36	.... =38

Sum Bingo

.... =22	.... =44
.... =38	.... =10
.... =80	.... =12

Cards for Sum Bingo

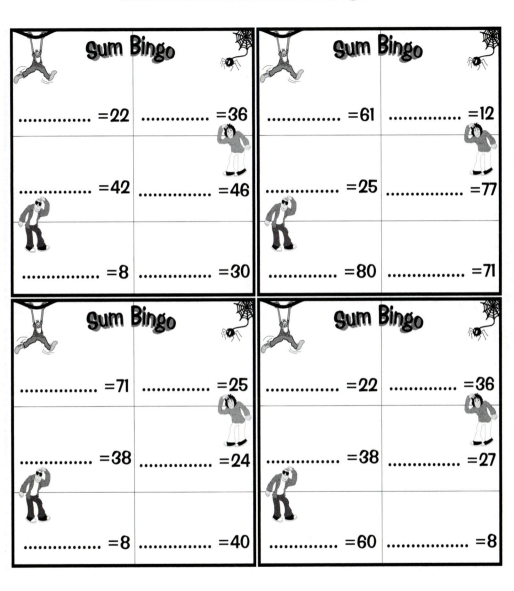

Sum Bingo

.... =22 .... =36

.... =42 .... =46

.... =8   .... =30

Sum Bingo

.... =61 .... =12

.... =25 .... =77

.... =80 .... =71

Sum Bingo

.... =71 .... =25

.... =38 .... =24

.... =8   .... =40

Sum Bingo

.... =22 .... =36

.... =38 .... =27

.... =60 .... =8

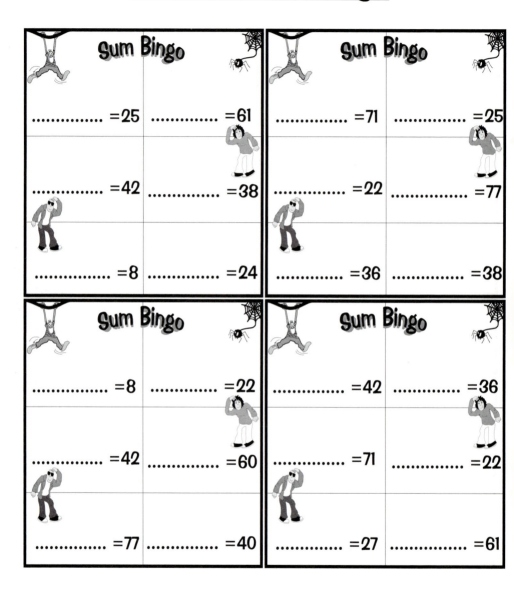

Cards for Sum Bingo

Sum Bingo

.... =25	.... =61
.... =42	.... =38
.... =8	.... =24

Sum Bingo

.... =71	.... =25
.... =22	.... =77
.... =36	.... =38

Sum Bingo

.... =8	.... =22
.... =42	.... =60
.... =77	.... =40

Sum Bingo

.... =42	.... =36
.... =71	.... =22
.... =27	.... =61

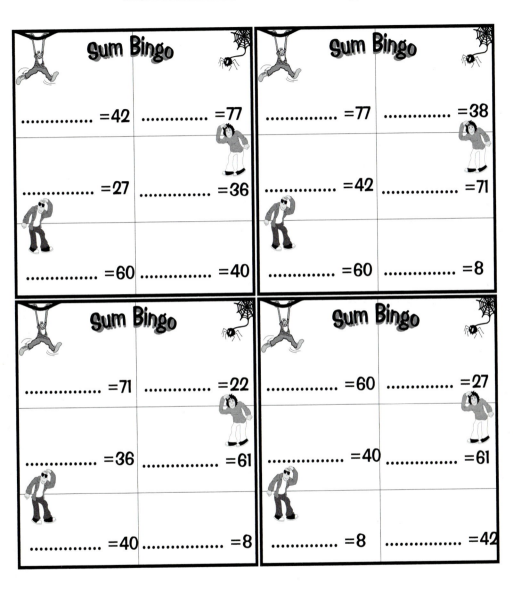

Cards for Sum Bingo

Sum Bingo

.... =42	.... =77
.... =27	.... =36
.... =60	.... =40

Sum Bingo

.... =77	.... =38
.... =42	.... =71
.... =60	.... =8

Sum Bingo

.... =71	.... =22
.... =36	.... =61
.... =40	.... =8

Sum Bingo

.... =60	.... =27
.... =40	.... =61
.... =8	.... =42

Snap and Memory

Maths: +, −, ×, ÷
Groups: Pairs or small groups
Equipment: Filled in photocopies of the blank cards opposite

What to do:

This is more of an idea for lots of activities than one specific activity. Photocopy the blank cards opposite and write sums on half of them and their answers on the other half. Then copy the cards again to get enough for everyone. The number of different sums doesn't matter, except that the more there are, the harder the games will be and the longer they'll take.

Here are two of the many games the cards could be used for:

Maths Snap:

Everyone gets into pairs. Each player is dealt a stack of cards. Players take it turns to put a card down in the middle of the table, face up. If the card played matches the one before (ie if they are a matching answer and sum), then the first player to say "SNAP" wins all of the cards in the pile, and adds them to their stack (you might also allow them to do this if two cards are identical — ie both the same sum or both the same answer).

If someone says "snap" when they don't match, the other person wins all of the cards in the pile.

The aim of the game is to get all of your opponent's cards from them — you win when they run out of cards.

Memory:

This is played in small groups. All of the cards are placed face down. The players take it in turns to turn two cards face up. If one is the answer to the other, they get to keep those cards. If not, those cards are turned back over again, but in the same place. The idea is that players try to remember where the cards are, so that when they find the other part, they can get the pair. When all of the cards have been picked up, whoever has the most wins.

Sum and Answer Cards

This page may be copied for use in the educational institution to which it was sold or sent only.

Sum Bingo 2 / Shape Bingo

<u>Maths</u>: +, −, ×, ÷
<u>Groups</u>: Whole class
<u>Equipment</u>: Photocopies of cards from pages 29-35

What to do:

Everyone has a copy of one of the bingo cards. You call out the answers below, one at a time, and fairly slowly. Then everyone has to work out if they have the sum with that answer. If so, they write the answer in the same square. The first person to fill in every gap on their card has to shout "bingo", and wins (assuming they haven't made any mistakes).

Not all answers are answers to only one sum.

Make sure you vary the order of the answers you call out, or the same card will always win.

Variations

Cards could be made up with easier or harder sums to suit the class. The blank cards on page 64 can be used for this.

The cards are graded in difficulty — the first cards are the easiest and they get progressively harder. This means pupils can be given cards to suit their ability.

The sums on the cards could be covered up with counters or small bits of paper when their answers have been called. That way the cards could be reused — but you wouldn't be able to see where someone had gone wrong.

All sorts of variations on the sums and answers are possible. One possibility is "<u>Shape Bingo</u>", using the cards provided on pages 36-42. Just call out the names of the shapes instead.

Answers to call out

18	19	20	17	6	8
63	12	41	96	18	21
13	40	9	23	36	24
7	51	22	31	55	

Cards for Sum Bingo 2

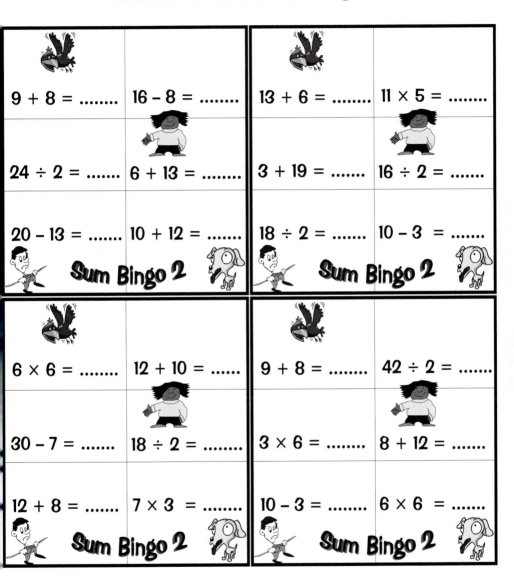

9 + 8 = ... | 16 – 8 = ...

24 ÷ 2 = ... | 6 + 13 = ...

20 – 13 = ... | 10 + 12 = ...

Sum Bingo 2

13 + 6 = ... | 11 × 5 = ...

3 + 19 = ... | 16 ÷ 2 = ...

18 ÷ 2 = ... | 10 – 3 = ...

Sum Bingo 2

6 × 6 = ... | 12 + 10 = ...

30 – 7 = ... | 18 ÷ 2 = ...

12 + 8 = ... | 7 × 3 = ...

Sum Bingo 2

9 + 8 = ... | 42 ÷ 2 = ...

3 × 6 = ... | 8 + 12 = ...

10 – 3 = ... | 6 × 6 = ...

Sum Bingo 2

Cards for Sum Bingo 2

36 ÷ 3 = ...	19 + 12 = ...
16 − 8 = ...	30 − 7 = ...
11 × 5 = ...	6 + 13 = ...

Sum Bingo 2

19 + 12 = ...	12 + 8 = ...
24 ÷ 2 = ...	3 × 6 = ...
30 − 7 = ...	55 − 15 = ...

Sum Bingo 2

16 − 8 = ...	7 × 9 = ...
19 + 12 = ...	3 + 19 = ...
6 × 3 = ...	18 ÷ 2 = ...

Sum Bingo 2

3 × 7 = ...	10 + 12 = ...
55 − 15 = ...	36 ÷ 3 = ...
9 × 7 = ...	9 + 8 = ...

Sum Bingo 2

Cards for Sum Bingo 2

20 – 13 = ... | 56 ÷ 7 = ...

24 ÷ 4 = ... | 24 + 17 = ...

8 × 3 = ... | 8 + 12 = ...

10 – 7 = ... | 9 + 8 = ...

19 + 12 = ... | 36 – 23 = ...

36 – 23 = ... | 6 × 6 = ...

Sum Bingo 2

Sum Bingo 2

13 + 6 = ... | 55 – 15 = ...

30 – 7 = ... | 7 × 9 = ...

11 × 5 = ... | 12 × 8 = ...

3 × 7 = ... | 12 + 8 = ...

42 ÷ 2 = ... | 25 + 26 = ...

19 + 3 = ... | 42 ÷ 6 = ...

Sum Bingo 2

Sum Bingo 2

Cards for Sum Bingo 2

8 + 9 = ...	6 × 3 = ...
30 – 7 = ...	36 – 23 = ...
24 + 17 = ...	42 ÷ 6 = ...

Sum Bingo 2

20 – 13 = ...	47 – 25 = ...
8 × 12 = ...	36 ÷ 3 = ...
12 + 10 = ...	25 + 26 = ...

Sum Bingo 2

42 ÷ 6 = ...	3 × 6 = ...
12 + 19 = ...	56 ÷ 7 = ...
3 × 8 = ...	36 – 23 = ...

Sum Bingo 2

24 ÷ 2 = ...	12 × 8 = ...
11 × 5 = ...	55 – 15 = ...
25 + 26 = ...	7 × 3 = ...

Sum Bingo 2

Cards for Sum Bingo 2

16 – 8 = ... | 24 ÷ 4 = ... | 3 × 8 = ... | 47 – 25 = ...

26 + 25 = ... | 8 × 3 = ... | 24 + 17 = ... | 36 – 23 = ...

36 ÷ 3 = ... | 10 – 3 = ... | 19 + 12 = ... | 24 ÷ 4 = ...

Sum Bingo 2

10 + 12 = ... | 56 ÷ 7 = ... | 24 ÷ 2 = ... | 24 ÷ 4 = ...

5 × 11 = ... | 8 × 12 = ... | 24 + 17 = ... | 9 × 7 = ...

55 – 15 = ... | 42 ÷ 6 = ... | 6 × 6 = ... | 47 – 25 = ...

Sum Bingo 2

Cards for Sum Bingo 2

19 + 12 = ...	55 – 15 = ...
12 × 8 = ...	24 ÷ 4 = ...
9 + 8 = ...	42 ÷ 6 = ...

Sum Bingo 2

8 + 12 = ...	8 × 12 = ...
6 × 6 = ...	36 ÷ 3 = ...
56 ÷ 7 = ...	13 + 6 = ...

Sum Bingo 2

24 ÷ 4 = ...	3 × 6 = ...
12 × 3 = ...	5 × 11 = ...
3 × 7 = ...	8 × 3 = ...

Sum Bingo 2

6 × 3 = ...	7 × 9 = ...
36 – 23 = ...	20 – 13 = ...
36 ÷ 3 = ...	55 – 15 = ...

Sum Bingo 2

Cards for Sum Bingo 2

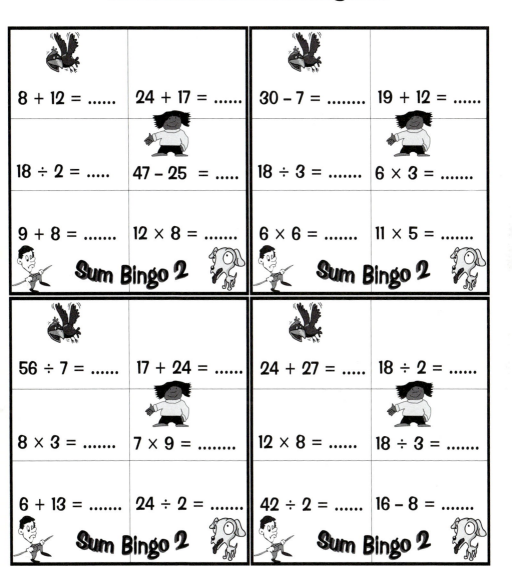

8 + 12 = ...   24 + 17 = ...

18 ÷ 2 = ...   47 – 25 = ...

9 + 8 = ...   12 × 8 = ...

Sum Bingo 2

30 – 7 = ...   19 + 12 = ...

18 ÷ 3 = ...   6 × 3 = ...

6 × 6 = ...   11 × 5 = ...

Sum Bingo 2

56 ÷ 7 = ...   17 + 24 = ...

8 × 3 = ...   7 × 9 = ...

6 + 13 = ...   24 ÷ 2 = ...

Sum Bingo 2

24 + 27 = ...   18 ÷ 2 = ...

12 × 8 = ...   18 ÷ 3 = ...

42 ÷ 2 = ...   16 – 8 = ...

Sum Bingo 2

Cards for Shape Bingo

Answers to call out

Right-angled triange   Square   Triangular prism
Circle   Pyramid   Rectangle
Cube   Cylinder   Sphere
                                     Isosceles triangle

Cards for Shape Bingo

Cards for Shape Bingo

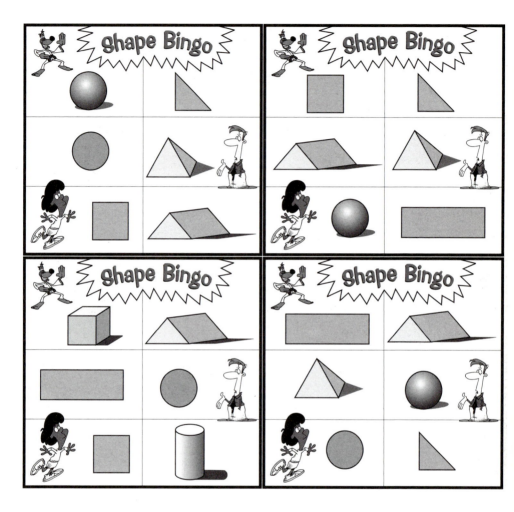

Cards for Shape Bingo

Cards for Shape Bingo

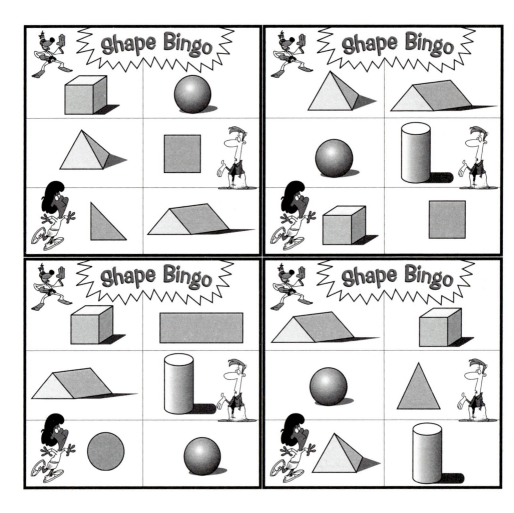

Cards for Shape Bingo

Cards for Shape Bingo

Rounding Game

<u>Maths</u>: Rounding numbers
<u>Groups</u>: Small groups
<u>Equipment</u>: Counters (different for each player), 10-sided spinners or dice, photocopy of the board over the page

Rules

First of all, each player needs some counters. The players take it in turns to throw both the dice or spin the spinners. They have to make a number from the two digits they get. There are two ways to do this:

1) By writing down the two digits in either order, rounding off to the nearest 10, and dividing by 10 (*ie* rounding and taking the left-hand digit)

2) By adding them together. If this is 9 or under, fine. If it's 10 or over, then take 10 away from it.

Then the player puts a counter on a square with that number on. If there's more than one square with the same number on, they get to choose where to put the counter. If a square already has another player's counter on, they can take it off and replace it with one of their own.

The winner is the first person to get four in a row.

Variations

Counters could remain on a square when additional counters are placed there, so that more than one player can occupy a square.

For a purely cosmetic change, instead of needing to get four in a row, they could need to get a T shape: three in a row with one attached to the middle, like this:

Decide at the beginning whether diagonals count or not. It's a little bit harder visually if they do.

Rounding Game Board

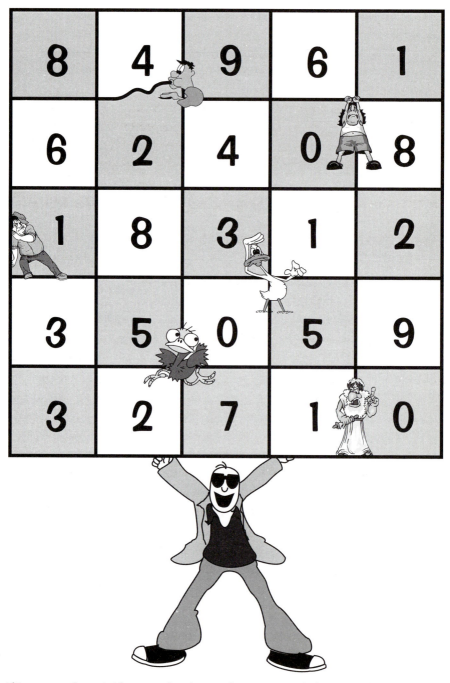

Treasure Hunt

Maths: Grids and coordinates
Groups: Pairs
Equipment: Photocopies of a map from page 46 or 47

What to do:

One player is the treasure hunter; the other has to hide his or her treasure (it can go on any square, including one with a picture). Both players get a copy of the map. The hider marks the treasure with an X on their own map, not letting the hunter see it. Then the treasure hunter calls out a grid reference. The hider calls out how close the other player is, using this scale:

"Boiling" — right next to it
"Warm" — in a 2-square ring around it
"Cold" — in a 3-square ring
"Freezing" — further away

The diagram on page 46 shows these distances.

The treasure hunter marks on his or her map where he or she checked for treasure, and how close it was, then guesses again. The treasure hunter wins when he or she finds the treasure by calling out its grid reference. Keep count of how many guesses it takes to find the treasure.

Variations

You could set a limit to how many goes the treasure hunter gets. For example the treasure hunter could have 10 goes to find the treasure. If they don't find it, the hider wins.

More advanced students could play a coordinate version. When the hunter calls out a pair of coordinates, the hider could use the special ruler on page 47 to say how warm the guess is.

Treasure Hunt Map 1

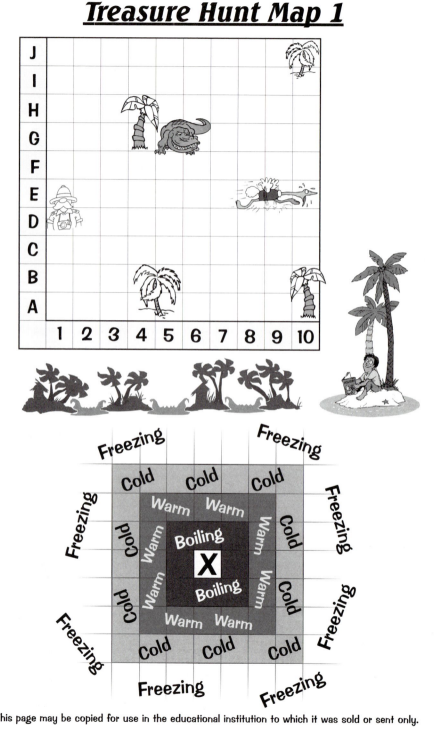

Treasure Hunt Map 2

Position and Direction

Maths: Position and direction
Groups: Small group or whole class
Equipment: A blindfold, gym mats / sheets of paper or equivalent

What to do:

You need to have a fair bit of space — a school hall would probably be best, though the game could be played outside.

It involves navigating around obstacles on the floor. Small gym mats would be ideal for the obstacles, but sheets of paper or other objects could be used. Whatever you use, make sure they're safe (paper on a polished floor could be slippery).

Place an obstacle on the floor. One person stands on this and wears a blindfold, or shuts their eyes. Then another obstacle is placed elsewhere; this is the goal. Lots of other obstacles are put on the ground between the first two.

The others take it in turns to guide the blindfolded one to the goal, by saying things like, "Three steps forward", "One step left", "Turn to the right", and so on. If the blindfolded one steps on an obstacle between the start and the goal, the person who gave him or her that direction is out. When the blindfolded one reaches the goal, the person who got them there becomes the next blindfolded one.

Variations

You could have a 'path' of mats leading from the start to the finish, preferably winding around a bit in between. The object would then be to stay on the mats and not touch the floor.

If you are short of space, the aim could be to get to the goal and back again (an object could be retrieved from the goal mat).

A similar game could be played on paper. Each player would be given a map in grid form and told a start position. You would give a series of directions for them to follow, then ask them for the grid reference of the final position. This could also be played in groups or pairs. Variations include the use of compass directions and coordinates instead of grid references.

Heights

<u>Maths</u>: Measures and ordering numbers
<u>Groups</u>: Small groups — about 5 per group
<u>Equipment</u>: Tape measures, height charts, metre rules

What to do:

Working in groups, the children measure each other, then each one writes their name and height on a large piece of card. Each group puts their heights in numerical order, then stands in that order to check they've got it right.

When all groups have done this the whole class stands in line, with everyone holding their card. Everyone gets into order of height. Then, starting at the shortest end, everyone calls out the number on their card. They all check that each number is bigger (or the same) as the one before.

Variations

The exercise could use metric or imperial units. To get a feel for their relative sizes, the class could be split into two groups, one working with each unit. Once the children are lined up, the heights in different units can be compared. Alternatively the metric group could line up first, then be shown someone's card with their height in feet and inches (and their name on the back, out of view). The group could try to work out where that person would go in the line. When decided, the name would be revealed and the person can stand in the predicted position — and see if it's right.

With a more advanced class, you could get the whole class to put their heights in order before standing in line.

You could also get them to compare lengths, by measuring the classroom, or their bedrooms, and work out how many of them would need to lie end to end to be as long as the room.

Maps / Directions

<u>Maths</u>: Position and direction
<u>Groups</u>: Whole class / small groups
<u>Equipment</u>: Photocopies of the map opposite

What to do:

This is a pencil and paper activity similar to the position and direction game on page 48. Each child is given a copy of the map opposite. One person in each group has the master map, on which they mark some treasure and 5 bombs (or holes or spiders etc. if you prefer). The idea is that the others in the group take it in turns to try to find the treasure without being blown up (or falling down a hole / being eaten etc.).

The players are allowed to move up, down, left or right — but not diagonally. Compass directions could be used if you prefer (if not then you might want to cover up the north arrow when you photocopy the map). Directions could be given either one square at a time, or with the number of squares specified (eg "two squares up"). They lose if the direction takes them over a bomb or lands them on a bomb — and it's the next person's go.

The players are not allowed to move over the pictures on the map — this makes tactical play possible by careful positioning of the bombs. The player positioning the treasure should make sure that it is possible to get to it from the start without crossing the pictures or bombs — otherwise the game will be impossible to win. The first person to find the treasure is the winner. The winner could become the next person to hide the treasure — or they could take it in turns.

Variations

Possibilities for varying the game include allowing diagonal moves, changing the number of bombs allowed, or using a different way to describe the moves (eg the use of angles — "turn 90° clockwise", "forward two squares" etc.). You could also allow them to move over the pictures on the grid, or jump bombs if they move over them without landing on them.

Maps / Directions

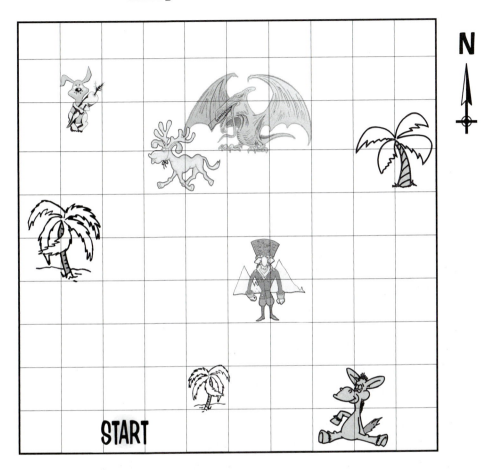

Further Variations

It isn't really necessary for everyone in each group to have a copy of the map — you could just have one for the person who hides the treasure, and one for the group trying to find it. You might want to allow the 'finders' to mark the position of bombs on their map — or you might prefer them to try to remember.

Another game that could be played with this or a similar grid would be to describe a path that traces out a shape, then ask the children what the shape is. Or you could ask the children to describe the path.

Battleships

<u>Maths</u>: Coordinates
<u>Groups</u>: Pairs
<u>Equipment</u>: Pencils, photocopies of page 53 (or page 54/55)

A good way to introduce coordinates without them even noticing.

Rules

There are two players. Each one has a double board from page 53 — one ship board and one missile board. Each player gets 6 ships:

2 tugs (2 squares)   1 aircraft carrier (4 squares)
2 destroyers (3 squares)   1 oil tanker (5 squares)

To begin with they colour in squares on their ship board to represent these ships (the ships can't be placed diagonally, but they can go over the pictures on a board).

They then take it in turns to fire missiles at each other's ships by giving the number and letter of a square. The opponent marks down the position of the missile on their ship board. If it hits a ship, they say "hit", otherwise they say "miss". If all the squares of a ship have been hit then the ship is sunk, and they should say "hit and sunk". The player who fired the missile puts a letter H or M on their missile board to show where they've fired. When a ship is sunk, a line is drawn through it on the ship board. The winner is the first person to sink all of their partner's ships.

Variations

You could use the map on page 54 with coordinates instead of grid references. The ships and hits / misses would be marked on the intersection of lines rather than in the squares.

Younger or less advanced students could use a number square (page 55) instead of coordinates. Or to make it really simple you could use a 5×5 board and 5 ships that are only one square each.

The game could be played in larger groups or as a whole class. The pupils could for example try to destroy the teacher's ships by taking it in turns to call out a square.

Game Board for Battleships

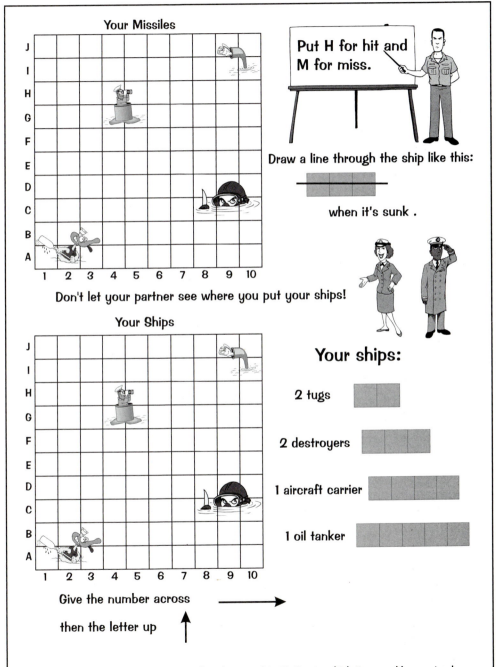

Your Missiles

Put H for hit and M for miss.

Draw a line through the ship like this:

when it's sunk .

Don't let your partner see where you put your ships!

Your Ships

Your ships:

2 tugs

2 destroyers

1 aircraft carrier

1 oil tanker

Give the number across

then the letter up

Game Board for Battleships

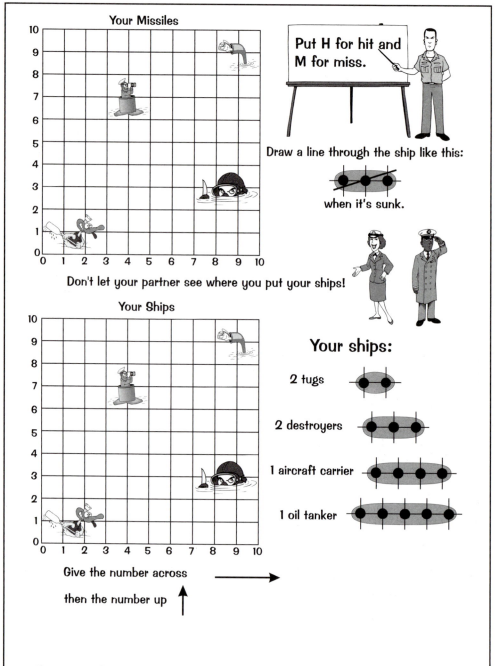

Your Missiles

Put H for hit and M for miss.

Draw a line through the ship like this:

when it's sunk.

Don't let your partner see where you put your ships!

Your Ships

Your ships:

2 tugs

2 destroyers

1 aircraft carrier

1 oil tanker

Give the number across

then the number up

Game Board for Battleships

Your Missiles

1	2	3	4	5	6	7	8	9	10
11	12	13	14	15	16	17	18	19	20
21	22	23	24	25	26	27	28	29	30
31	32	33	34	35	36	37	38	39	40
41	42	43	44	45	46	47	48	49	50
51	52	53	54	55	56	57	58	59	60
61	62	63	64	65	66	67	68	69	70
71	72	73	74	75	76	77	78	79	80
81	82	83	84	85	86	87	88	89	90
91	92	93	94	95	96	97	98	99	100

Put H for hit and M for miss.

Draw a line through the ship like this:

when it's sunk.

Don't let your partner see where you put your ships!

Your Ships

1	2	3	4	5	6	7	8	9	10
11	12	13	14	15	16	17	18	19	20
21	22	23	24	25	26	27	28	29	30
31	32	33	34	35	36	37	38	39	40
41	42	43	44	45	46	47	48	49	50
51	52	53	54	55	56	57	58	59	60
61	62	63	64	65	66	67	68	69	70
71	72	73	74	75	76	77	78	79	80
81	82	83	84	85	86	87	88	89	90
91	92	93	94	95	96	97	98	99	100

Your ships:

2 tugs

2 destroyers

1 aircraft carrier

1 oil tanker

Unfolding Packets / Shape Nets

Maths: Shape nets
Groups: Pairs or individuals
Equipment: Scissors, glue or sticky tape; photocopies from pages 57-61

What to do:

Taking apart a cereal packet is a good way to show the class how solids can be made from shape nets. Having done that the class can dive into making their own...

Photocopy the nets you're going to use from pages 57-61. The nets vary in difficulty, so some will be better suited to particular children.

Once made, the shapes could be decorated or put to use. In particular the cube could be used to make dice — which could be used in games.

Variations

By enlarging when photocopying, you could make bigger shapes.

Alternatively, you could challenge them to draw the nets themselves. The chances are they might be a bit wonky though. This way you could make an absolutely _huge_ shape, and hang it from the ceiling.

Another thing you could do to help them visualise shapes is to show them a shape net and ask them what shape they think it will make. You could point to a side on a cuboid shape net and ask them which side it will be opposite. You could even tell them that opposite sides of a dice always add up to 7 — then ask them to draw the numbers or dots on before they put it together.

Shape Net — for a Cube

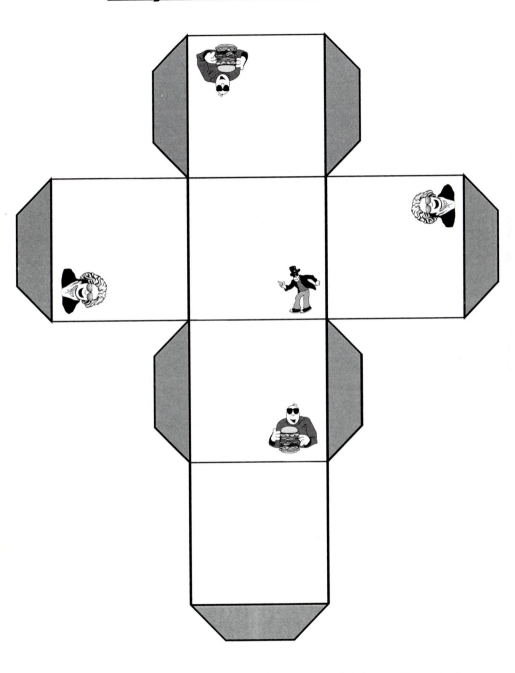

58

Shape Net — for a Triangular Prism

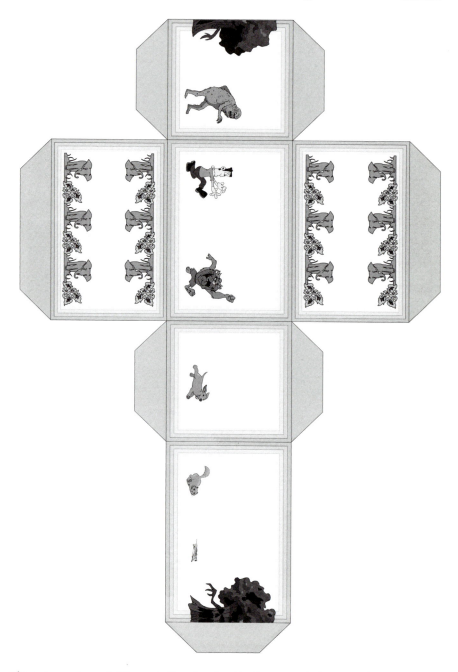

Shape Net — for a Tetrahedron

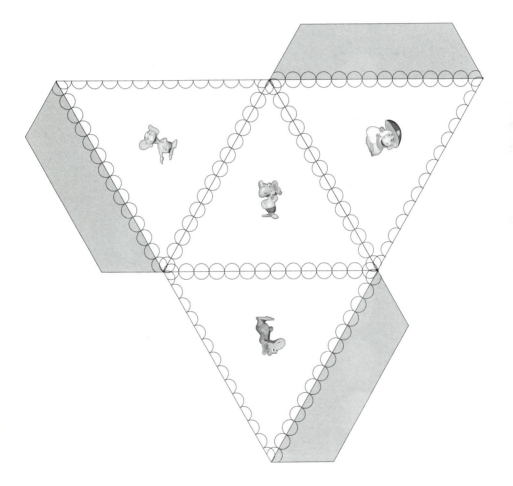

Shape Net — for a Triangular Prism

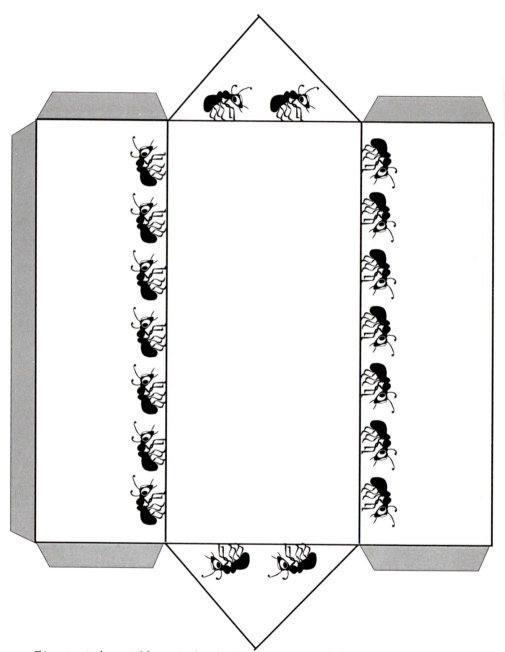

Shape Net — for a Pyramid

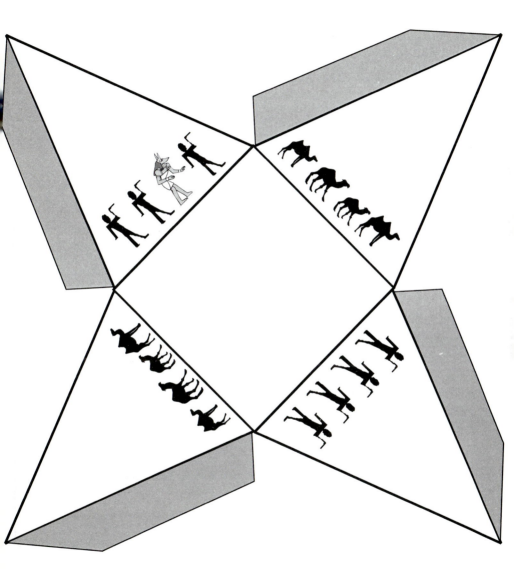

Venn Diagrams

<u>Maths</u>: Venn diagrams
<u>Groups</u>: Whole class
<u>Equipment</u>: Rope / string / hula hoops

What to do:

It's easier to teach things like Venn diagrams if pupils have clear pictures of them. This is a good way to achieve that. The idea is that you create a huge Venn diagram on the floor or a table. The rope, string or hula hoops can be used for the boundaries of the sets.

The diagram could display all sorts of things — *eg* the two sets could be labelled "triangles" and "shapes with right angles". You could ask each child to draw and cut out a shape, then place it in the correct part of the diagram.

Variations

You could make the diagram much bigger and more interactive by having the children *in* the diagram. The sets could be marked out with rope on the playground or the classroom floor, then the children could take it in turns to step into the correct area. You could for example use it to show siblings — one set could be for those with brothers and the other for those with sisters. Those with both would then be in the intersection and 'only children' around the outside.

Children's pets could be shown. The children could be sorted into those with cats, those with dogs, and those with other pets.

The idea could be combined with other areas of maths — properties of numbers, for example. Each child could be given a card with a number, and the diagram could show something like multiples of 3 and multiples of 5. Each child would either stand in or place their card in the correct set. The cards supplied for the differences game (pages 15-17) could be used for this — or you could adapt the blank cards on page 27. Alternatively they could each be given a number to write on their own piece of paper.

Block Graphs

<u>Maths</u>: Block graphs
<u>Groups</u>: Whole class
<u>Equipment</u>: Rope / string / metre ruler — and paper or building
blocks

What to do:

Block graphs could be made in a very similar way to the Venn
diagrams described on the previous page. Either string or metre
rulers could be used for the axes, then 'blocks' could be placed
to build up the columns. These blocks could be just pieces of
paper placed across the floor or table (A4 sheets folded into four
might work well — or you could use unfolded A4 or A5 sheets).

You could display similar things to the Venn diagrams — and
showing the same data in both formats would be a good way to
show the differences between them. You could show the *number*
of siblings of each child — so the horizontal axis would be
labelled 0, 1, 2 etc. With pets you could have a column for each
different type of pet.

Variations

Objects instead of paper could be used to build up the
columns — a bit like a pictogram. If you had suitable building
blocks then you could even make a vertical block graph.

This is an ideal opportunity to introduce block graphs (or Venn
diagrams) on paper. Once you've created one, copy it onto the
board and point out how the drawing relates to the one the class
made.

As with the Venn diagram on the previous page, you could
also make a much larger version with the children sitting in lines
to form the columns. It might be easier to appreciate it if you're
not actually in it though — in which case the class could be
divided into two groups (*eg* boys and girls), and each group
could form their block graph in turn.

Blank Bingo Cards

Bingo

Bingo

Bingo

Bingo

MHT20